THE
LITTLEST ANGEL

Abridged

Story by CHARLES TAZEWELL
Illustrated by KATHERINE EVANS

WONDER BOOKS • NEW YORK

This is my

WONDER BOOK

....

THE LITTLEST ANGEL was exactly four years, six months, five days, seven hours and forty-two minutes of age when he presented himself to the Gate-Keeper and waited for admittance to the Glorious Kingdom of God.

The Littlest Angel tried to pretend that he wasn't at all afraid. But his lower lip trembled, and a tear ran down to the very tip end of his small freckled nose. He also sniffled — a most unangelic sound which so unnerved the good Gate-Keeper that he did something he had never done before in all Eternity. He blotted the page!

From that moment on, the Heavenly Peace was never quite the same, and the Littlest Angel soon became the despair of all the Heavenly Host. His shrill, ear-splitting whistle resounded at all hours through the Golden Streets, and he sang off-key at the singing practice of the Heavenly Choir.

And, being so small that it seemed to take him just twice as long as anyone else to get to nightly prayers, the Littlest Angel always arrived late, and always knocked everyone's wings askew as he darted into his place.

It was first whispered among the Seraphim and Cherubim, and then said aloud among the Angels and Archangels, that he didn't even look like an angel! And they were all quite correct. He didn't. His halo was permanently tarnished where he held onto it when he ran, and he was always running. Even when he stood still, it was always slipping down over his right eye. Or over his left eye. Or else, just for pure meanness, slipping off the back of his head and rolling away down some Golden Street just so he'd have to chase after it!

Yes, and it must be here recorded that his wings were neither useful nor ornamental. All Paradise held its breath when the Littlest Angel perched himself like a fledgling sparrow on the very edge of a gilded cloud and prepared to take off.

He would teeter this way — and that way — but, after much coaxing and a few false starts, he would shut both of his eyes, hold his freckled nose, count up to three hundred and three, and then hurl himself slowly into space! However, owing to the regrettable fact that he always forgot to move his wings, the Littlest Angel always fell head over halo!

It was also reported, and never denied, that whenever he was nervous, which was most of the time, he bit his wing-tips!

Now, anyone can easily understand why the Littlest Angel would, soon or late, have to be disciplined. And so, on an Eternal Day of an Eternal Month in the Year Eternal, he was directed to present his small self before an Angel of the Peace.

The Littlest Angel combed his hair, dusted his wings and scrambled into an almost clean robe, and then, with a heavy heart, trudged his way to the place of judgment. He removed his halo and breathed upon it heavily, then polished it upon his robe, and t i p · t o e d in!

The Understanding Angel looked down at the small culprit. "So you're the one who's been making Heaven so unheavenly!" he chuckled. "Come here, Cherub, and tell me all about it!"

Suddenly, almost before he knew it, the Littlest Angel was perched on the lap of the understanding Angel, and was explaining how very difficult it was for a boy who suddenly finds himself an angel. Yes, he'd swung three times on the Golden Gates. But that was just for something to do! That was the whole trouble. There wasn't anything for a small angel to do. And he was very homesick.

Oh, not that Paradise wasn't beautiful! But the Earth was beautiful, too! Wasn't it created by God, Himself? Why, there were trees to climb, and brooks to fish, and caves to play at pirate chief, the swimming hole, and sun, and rain, and dark, and dawn, and thick brown dust, so soft and warm beneath your feet!

The Understanding Angel smiled, and in his eyes was a long forgotten memory of another small boy in a long ago. Then he asked the Littlest Angel what would make him most happy in Paradise. The Cherub thought for a moment.

"There's a box. I left it under my bed back home. If only I could have that!" he whispered in his ear.

The Understanding Angel nodded his head. "You shall have it," he promised. And a fleet-winged Heavenly messenger was instantly dispatched to bring the box to Paradise.

Then it came to pass that Jesus, the Son of God, was to be born. And as the glorious tidings spread through Paradise, all the angels rejoiced. The Angels and Archangels, the Seraphim and Cherubim, the Gate-Keeper, the Wingmaker, yes, and even the Halosmith put aside their usual tasks to prepare their gifts for the Blessed Infant. All but the Littlest Angel. He sat down on the Golden Stairs and waited for inspiration.

The time of the Miracle was very close at hand when the Littlest Angel at last decided on his gift. Then, on that Day of

Days, he proudly brought it from its hiding place behind a cloud, and humbly, with downcast eyes, placed it before the Throne of God. It was only a small, rough, unsightly box, but inside were all those wonderful things that even a Child of God would treasure!

A small, rough, unsightly box, lying among all those other glorious gifts from all the Angels of Paradise! Gifts of such rare and breathless beauty that Heaven and all the Universe were lighted by the mere reflection of their glory! And when the Littlest Angel saw this, he suddenly wished he might reclaim his shabby gift. It was ugly. It was worthless. If only he could hide it away from the sight of God before it was even noticed!

But it was too late! The Hand of God moved slowly over all the bright array of shining gifts, then paused, then dropped, then came to rest on the lowly gift of the Littlest Angel!

The Littlest Angel trembled as the box was opened, and there, before the Eyes of God and all His Heavenly Host, was what he offered to the Christ Child.

And what was his gift to the Blessed Infant? Well, there was a butterfly with golden wings, captured one bright summer day, a sky-blue egg from a bird's nest, and two white stones, found on a muddy river bank, where he and his friends had played like small brown beavers. At the bottom of the box was a limp, tooth-marked leather strap, once worn as a collar by his dog.

The Littlest Angel wept hot, bitter tears, for now he knew that instead of honoring the Son of God, he had been most blasphemous.

Why had he ever thought the box was so wonderful?

Why had he dreamed that such utterly useless things would be loved by the Blessed Infant?

In frantic terror, he turned to run and hide from the Divine Wrath of the Heavenly Father, but he stumbled and fell to the very foot of the Heavenly Throne!

There was a dreadful silence in the Celestial City, a silence complete and undisturbed save for the heartbroken sobbing of the Littlest Angel. Then, suddenly, the Voice of God, like Divine Music, rose and swelled through Paradise!

And the Voice of God spoke, saying, "Of all the gifts of all the Angels, I find that this small box pleases Me most. Its contents are of the Earth and of Men, and My Son is born to be King of both. These are the things My Son, too, will know and love and cherish, and then leave behind Him when His task is done. I accept this gift in the Name of the Child, Jesus, born of Mary this night in Bethlehem."

There was a breathless pause, and then the rough, unsightly box of the Littlest Angel began to glow. The light became a radiant brilliance that blinded the eyes of all the angels!

None but the Littlest Angel saw it rise from its place before the Throne of God. And only he watched it shed its clear, white, beckoning light over a Stable where a Child was born.

There it shone on that Night of Miracles, and its light was reflected down the centuries deep in the heart of all mankind. Yet, earthly eyes, blinded, too, by its splendor, could never know that the lowly gift of the Littlest Angel was what all men would call forever *The Shining Star of Bethlehem!*